SNOOPY

by Charles M. Schulz

Freewheelin'

Ravette London

D1416424

This edition first published by
Ravette Limited 1987
Reprinted 1987

Printed and bound in Great Britain
for Ravette Limited,
3 Glenside Estate, Star Road, Partridge Green,
Horsham, Sussex RH13 8RA
by The Guernsey Press Company Limited,
Guernsey, Channel Islands.

ISBN 0 948456 86 8

Freewheelin'

He's cool, he's witty and he's sophisticated. He's Snoopy. He sleeps on top of his kennel, he submits manuscripts to publishers, conducts philosophical discussions with a little bird known as Woodstock, he's a master of disguise and an all-round sporting hero. As you can see, he's not your average beagle. In fact, Snoopy is anything but average! He's a freewheelin' spirit!

AS LONG AS WE'RE JUST PRACTICING, I HAVE A SUGGESTION

MAYBE YOU SHOULD SHOOT AT THE OTHER GOAL FOR A WHILE...

12-27

WHEN ABRAHAM LINCOLN WAS AN ATTORNEY, HE WOULD ARRIVE AT HIS OFFICE AT NINE O'CLOCK

HE WOULD IMMEDIATELY STRETCH OUT ON THE COUCH, AND MUCH TO HIS PARTNER'S ANNOYANCE, BEGIN TO READ THE NEWSPAPERS OUT LOUD

I'LL HAVE TO REMEMBER THAT

THE SECRET TO BEING A GOOD ATTORNEY IS TO ANNOY YOUR PARTNER

12-28

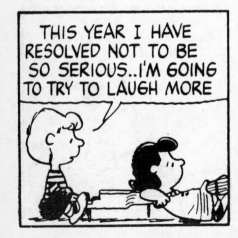

WE CAN'T STAND HERE FOREVER, SIR

OKAY! LET'S MAKE A RUN FOR IT!!

HAVE YOU CALLED THE ROLL YET, MA'AM?

1-5-83

WELL, WHEN YOU GET TO "TWO DROWNED RATS," WE'RE PRESENT!

YOU'RE WANTED ON THE TELEPHONE

RATS

TELL THEM I'M BUSY

I'LL JUST TELL THEM YOU'RE SLEEPING

SLEEPING IS BUSY!

1-6-83

NO, MA'AM, I DON'T KNOW THE ANSWER...

© 1982 United Feature Syndicate, Inc.

1-7-83

I FELT SMART WHEN I WOKE UP THIS MORNING..

BUT THEN IT STARTED TO SNOW WHILE I WAS WALKING TO SCHOOL...

ALL THOSE SNOWFLAKES COOLED DOWN MY BRAIN!

I KNOW YOU LOVE YOUR PIANO MORE THAN YOU LOVE ME

I CAN LIVE WITH THAT

1-8-83

WHO KNOWS? MAYBE SOMEDAY THINGS WILL CHANGE

© 1982 United Feature Syndicate, Inc.

I'M HAPPY JUST BEING IN THE "ON DECK CIRCLE"

I THINK I'VE LOST MY PICTURE

1-21

THAT'S A WEIRD-LOOKING SNOWMAN

NOT SO WEIRD...HE'S JUST COME IN FROM WORKING IN THE SNOWFIELDS

AND SEE WHAT'S IN HIS HAND?

A NICE COLD GLASS OF SNOW!

1-22

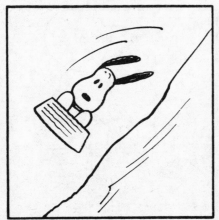

DON'T YOU THINK SO?

© 1983 United Feature Syndicate, Inc.

ABSOLUTELY NOT!

1/26

BUT I CAN UNDERSTAND WHY YOU BELIEVE THAT

WHEN I WAS YOUR AGE, I WAS DUMB, TOO

1-27

© 1983 United Feature Syndicate, Inc.

WHAT'S WRONG WITH HIM?

2-2

MAYBE HE KNOWS SOMETHING WE DON'T KNOW..

ANIMALS WILL SOMETIMES BEHAVE IRRATIONALLY WHEN THEY SENSE AN ONCOMING EARTHQUAKE...

OR WHEN THE PIZZA WAS TOO HOT!

PSYCHIATRIC HELP 5¢

THE DOCTOR IS IN

I WANT TO ASK YOU SOMETHING

ARE THERE ANY SELF-IMPROVEMENT BOOKS THAT YOU WOULD RECOMMEND?

2-3

FOR YOURSELF?

HOW ABOUT SOMETHING IN TWENTY-FOUR VOLUMES?

THE DOCTOR

Dear Valentine,

Just a few words to tell you how much I love you.

I have loved you since the first day I saw you.

Whenever that was.

2-7

Dear Valentine,

I have thought of you often.

2-8

Not all the time, but often.

© 1983 United Feature Syndicate, Inc.

THIS IS THE MEDICINE THAT THE VET SAID WOULD BE GOOD FOR YOU

I HAVE ALSO HEARD, HOWEVER, THAT LAUGHTER IS THE BEST MEDICINE...

WHICH WOULD YOU PREFER?

HA HA HA HA!

THAT WAS EASY

2-21

HERE, YOU GOT A MESSAGE FROM YOUR BROTHER SPIKE...

"NEED HELP! AM SURROUNDED BY COYOTES! CANNOT HOLD OUT MUCH LONGER!"

2-22

SPIKE NEEDS HELP! TO ARMS!!

ALL RIGHT... TO WINGS!

HERE'S THE WORLD FAMOUS SERGEANT-MAJOR LEADING HIS TROOPS TO NEEDLES TO SAVE HIS BROTHER WHO IS SURROUNDED BY COYOTES...

WE'LL HAVE TO HURRY, MEN! WE DON'T KNOW HOW LONG POOR SPIKE CAN HOLD OUT...

SPIKE WON'T GIVE UP WITHOUT A FIGHT, THOUGH.. HE'LL TAKE WHATEVER THEY THROW AT HIM!

NO FAIR SHOOTING RUBBER BANDS!

© 1983 United Feature Syndicate, Inc.

2-23

SCHULZ

THE TROOPS ARE TIRED..WE'LL HAVE TO CAMP HERE TONIGHT

2-24

EAT YOUR FIRECAKE, MEN, AND THEN TRY TO GET A GOOD NIGHT'S SLEEP...WE STILL HAVE A LONG WAY TO GO...

POOR SPIKE, ALL ALONE, SURROUNDED BY COYOTES, FIGHTING FOR HIS LIFE...

© 1983 United Feature Syndicate, Inc.   SCHULZ

ALL RIGHT, IF YOU'RE GONNA SHOOT RUBBER BANDS AT ME, I'M GONNA SHOOT 'EM BACK!

OKAY, MEN, MOVE OUT! WE HAVE A LONG WAY TO GO, BUT SPIKE NEEDS OUR HELP!

I WONDER HOW HE'S DOING OUT THERE IN THE DESERT ALL ALONE FIGHTING OFF THE COYOTES

2-25 © 1983 United Feature Syndicate, Inc.

FORTUNATELY, SPIKE IS A REAL FIGHTER... HE KNOWS ALL THE TRICKS..

OW!

RATS! IT'S HARD TO SHOOT A RUBBER BAND WITHOUT HITTING YOUR OWN FINGERS!

HOW DO WE KNOW WHERE WE'RE GOING? WE FOLLOW THE MOON!

2-26

REMEMBER, THE MOON IS ALWAYS OVER HOLLYWOOD, AND NEEDLES ISN'T FAR FROM HOLLYWOOD

NO, OLIVIER, IF WE GET NEAR PARIS, WE CAN'T STOP...

© 1983 United Feature Syndicate, Inc.

THERE IT IS, MEN.. THE FANTASTIC LITTLE TOWN OF NEEDLES!

AND SOMEWHERE OUT THERE IN THE DESERT, MY BROTHER, SPIKE, IS SURROUNDED BY COYOTES... WE HAVE TO RESCUE HIM!

2-28

ALL RIGHT, I NEED ONE VOLUNTEER TO ACT AS SCOUT....

© 1983 United Feature Syndicate, Inc.

NO, YOU CAN'T VOLUNTEER HARRIET BECAUSE SHE ISN'T HERE

OKAY, BILL, I WANT YOU TO SNEAK OUT THERE, AND FIND MY BROTHER, SPIKE..

IF YOU SEE ANY COYOTES, COME BACK HERE, AND TELL US WHAT THEY'RE DOING

I DON'T KNOW.. I NEVER THOUGHT ABOUT IT...

3-1

ANYONE HERE KNOW WHAT A COYOTE LOOKS LIKE?

CHOP CHOP CHOP CHOP

CHOP CHOP CHOP CHOP

CHOP CHOP CHOP CHOP

JUST DROP ME OFF AT MY REAL ESTATE OFFICE.. I HAVE SOME PAPERS THAT NEED TO BE SIGNED

BEFORE WE LEAVE, SPIKE, TELL ME WHY THE COYOTES WERE SO MAD AT YOU...

SPIKE'S REAL ESTATE

"OCEAN VIEW CONDOMINIUMS FOR SALE, CHEAP"

YOU TRIED TO SELL OCEAN VIEW CONDOMINIUMS IN THE MIDDLE OF THE DESERT?

I FIGURED THAT COYOTES COULD SEE A LONG WAY

© 1983 United Feature Syndicate, Inc.   3-9

3-10

© 1983 United Feature Syndicate, Inc.

CAN YOU IMAGINE THAT? WE MARCH ALL THE WAY OUT HERE TO RESCUE MY BROTHER FROM THE COYOTES, AND YOU KNOW WHY?

ALL BECAUSE OF SOME REAL ESTATE DEAL... HOW CAN YOU SELL CONDOMINIUMS TO A BUNCH OF COYOTES?

3-11

© 1983 United Feature Syndicate, Inc.

ANYWAY, MEN, YOU DID A GOOD JOB, AND WHEN WE GET BACK, I'LL PUT YOU IN FOR A UNIT CITATION AND A THREE-DAY PASS...

NO, OLIVIER, YOU'D NEVER MAKE IT TO PARIS ON A THREE-DAY PASS

SCHULZ

I SEE YOUR STUPID DOG HAS FINALLY COME BACK HOME

I DON'T SEE HOW HE FINDS HIS WAY AROUND LIKE HE DOES...

© 1983 United Feature Syndicate, Inc.

DOGS HAVE A FANTASTIC SENSE OF DIRECTION AND VERY GOOD MEMORIES

IS THIS WHERE I LIVE?

SCHULZ 3-12

HEY, CHUCK..HOW WOULD YOU LIKE TO HELP OUT MY BASEBALL TEAM THIS YEAR?

WE REALLY NEED SOMEONE LIKE YOU, CHUCK...

BUT WHAT ABOUT MY OWN TEAM?

© 1983 United Feature Syndicate, Inc.

3-16

IT WOULD BREAK THEIR HEARTS IF I LEFT THEM

IT WOULD?

YOU DID IT, DIDN'T YOU, SIR? YOU CALLED CHUCK, AND YOU TOLD HIM THAT OUR TEAM NEEDS HIM!

© 1983 United Feature Syndicate, Inc.

WELL, WE DO, MARCIE

YES, BUT NOT FOR WHAT HE THINKS!

HE THINKS HE'S GOING TO BE THE PITCHER OR PLAY RIGHT WING, OR LINEBACKER OR GOALIE OR SOMETHING!

3-17

LOOK, MARCIE, YOU'VE GOT ME SO UPSET MY HAIR IS FALLING OUT

IT'S EITHER A THYROID PROBLEM OR GUILT, SIR

YOUR JOB, CHUCK, WILL BE TO JUMP AROUND AND GET OUR FANS TO CHEER

YOU HAVE FANS?

© 1983 United Feature Syndicate, Inc.

AND WHEN ONE OF US HITS A HOME RUN, WE WANT YOU TO TURN SOMERSAULTS, JUMP UP AN' DOWN AND GO CRAZY!

YOU HIT HOME RUNS?

3-23

TOMORROW'S OUR FIRST GAME, CHUCK... I WANT YOU TO GO HOME AND GET A GOOD REST...

BUT DON'T TAKE YOUR COSTUME OFF! I WANT YOU TO THINK PELICAN AND BE PELICAN!

3-24

© 1983 United Feature Syndicate, Inc.

"THINK PELICAN.. BE PELICAN..."

CHARLIE BROWN? WHAT'S THIS ABOUT YOU BEING A MASCOT ON PEPPERMINT PATTY'S BASEBALL TEAM?

I HEAR SHE'S GOT YOU WEARING A DUMB PELICAN COSTUME...AND SHE WANTS YOU TO WEAR IT ALL THE TIME...

WHAT DID YOU SAY? YOUR VOICE SOUNDS MUFFLED...WHY DOES YOUR VOICE SOUND MUFFLED?

3-25

IT'S HARD TO EXPLAIN...

MARCIE! WHAT ARE YOU DOING HERE?

I WANT YOU TO TAKE OFF THAT STUPID COSTUME, CHARLES, AND STOP LETTING YOURSELF BE HUMILIATED!

3-26

IF YOU WON'T DO IT FOR YOURSELF, DO IT FOR SOMEONE WHO LIKES YOU

KISS HER, YOU BLOCKHEAD!

This is my report on Charles Dickens. I did not know Charles Dickens personally.

If I had known him personally, I would not be here now and would not be writing this report.

© 1983 United Feature Syndicate, Inc.   4-8

© 1983 United Feature Syndicate, Inc.
4-9

YOU'RE WELCOME!

THAT WAS VERY NICE

WHEN THE MATCH WAS OVER, THEY ALSO THANKED ALL THE BALL-BEAGLES

NOTICE ANYTHING?

LIKE WHAT?

MY BLANKET IS GONE!! I'VE GIVEN IT UP! I DON'T NEED IT ANYMORE!

4-11

WHEN DID THIS HAPPEN?

FOUR MINUTES AGO!

YOU DON'T THINK I'VE GIVEN UP MY BLANKET, DO YOU?

YOU THINK I'M WEAK...

YOU THINK I HAVE NO WILLPOWER!

4-12

WAS IT HARD GETTING THE BLANKET INTO YOUR LUNCH BOX?

OOO! A FOUR-LEAF CLOVER!

BONK!

© 1983 United Feature Syndicate, Inc.

HEY, MANAGER, GUESS WHAT I JUST FOUND...

WELL, IT SURE WASN'T A FLY BALL!

4-27

HE'S TERRIBLE AT GUESSING GAMES..IT TOOK HIM NINE TRIES BEFORE HE GUESSED...

SCHULZ

I SAW SOMETHING FUNNY ON TV LAST NIGHT

4-28

THIS BASEBALL TEAM HAD A REAL LOUDMOUTH ON IT... THE MANAGER COULDN'T TAKE IT, SO HE PULLED THE LOUDMOUTH'S CAP DOWN OVER HIS HEAD!

I WONDER IF THAT WOULD EVER HAPPEN IN REAL LIFE...

I GUESS IT COULD

SCHULZ

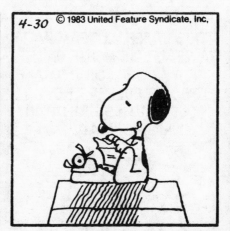

YOU SHOULD TRY WRITING AN ADVENTURE STORY

5-2

TRY WRITING ABOUT A REAL HERO TYPE

© 1983 United Feature Syndicate, Inc.

He was a dark and stormy knight.

THE THIRD QUESTION? I PUT DOWN,"YES OR NO"

© 1983 United Feature Syndicate, Inc.

"Yesorno"

5-3

YOU'RE PROBABLY RIGHT, MARCIE, BUT IT SURE LOOKS WEIRD

THERE'S A WOMAN WHO LIVES UP IN THE NEXT BLOCK WHO ALWAYS HAS TOAST FOR BREAKFAST

EACH MORNING, SHE TOSSES OUT A FEW CRUMBS FOR THE BIRDS..IF YOU GOT UP EARLY, YOU COULD BE THE FIRST ONE THERE

© 1983 United Feature Syndicate, Inc.

5-4

NO, I DON'T THINK I COULD TALK HER INTO BRINGING THEM DOWN HERE

IT'S SUPPERTIME! AND DO I EVER HAVE A SURPRISE FOR YOU!

TONIGHT I'M BRINGING YOUR SUPPER IN FROM A DIFFERENT DIRECTION!

I GUESS I'M ONE OF THE LUCKY ONES

5-5 © 1983 United Feature Syndicate, Inc.

ALL MY LIFE EXCITING THINGS HAVE BEEN HAPPENING TO ME!

© 1983 United Feature Syndicate, Inc. 5-6

© 1983 United Feature Syndicate, Inc.

5-7

"VALLEY" IS THE WORD!

IF YOU WANT TO WRITE A BESTSELLER, YOU HAVE TO USE "VALLEY" IN THE TITLE...

5-16

© 1983 United Feature Syndicate, Inc.

Valley of the Beagles

WHAT'S THIS?

THE OL' RABBIT HOUND IS IN ACTION, HUH?

HAVE YOU SEEN ANY RABBITS?

© 1983 United Feature Syndicate, Inc.

WHO DO YOU THINK IS CHASING ME?

5-17

WHY DON'T YOU SAY IT?

IF YOU HAVE AN OX TO GRIND, JUST SAY SO!

IT MAKES A DIFFERENCE WHOSE AX IS GORED, DOESN'T IT?

© 1983 United Feature Syndicate, Inc.

I NEVER KNOW WHAT YOU'RE TALKING ABOUT

GOING FISHING, HUH?

THAT'S A GREAT-LOOKING HAT

© 1983 United Feature Syndicate, Inc.

BUT I DON'T KNOW ABOUT THE FISHING POLE

5-30

© 1983 United Feature Syndicate, Inc.

YES, SIR...IF I MAY, I'D LIKE TO RETURN THIS KITE

I THINK IT'S AFRAID OF HEIGHTS!

© 1983 United Feature Syndicate, Inc.

5-31

MAYBE YOU'LL BE LUCKY AND IT WON'T RAIN TONIGHT

INSTEAD OF JUST STANDING THERE, WHY DON'T YOU GET SOMEONE TO HELP ME?

6-3

AARRGH!

THERE'S A GIRL I KNOW AT SCHOOL WHO HAS AN OLDER BROTHER WHO SHE'S ACTUALLY NOT ASHAMED OF

IS THAT YOU, BIG BROTHER?

MOM SAYS FOR YOU TO TAKE A BATH BEFORE DINNER

6-4

THERE'S SOAP AND A TOWEL AND CLEAN CLOTHES BY THE SINK..

AND A SCISSORS...

SO HERE I AM, RIDING ON THE BACK OF MOM'S TEN-SPEED...

6-6

PEOPLE WONDER WHY I WEAR A SKI CAP WHEN IT'S SO WARM OUTSIDE

LOOK OUT FOR THE TRUCK! LOOK OUT FOR THE CAR!

I NEED IT FOR GOING THROUGH TRAFFIC

© 1983 United Feature Syndicate, Inc.

I'VE NEVER LOANED ANYONE A PAIR OF SHOES BEFORE, SIR

DON'T WORRY, MARCIE... I'LL TAKE GOOD CARE OF THEM

6-7

DON'T GET THEM DIRTY

I WON'T

TRY NOT TO TOUCH THE GROUND WHEN YOU WALK!

© 1983 United Feature Syndicate, Inc.

HEY, MANAGER..

NOW WHAT?

I THINK YOUR DOG IS AFRAID OF THUNDER

I GOT A "C" IN MATH, A "C" IN HISTORY, A "C" IN SPELLING...

AND WHAT'S THIS?

AN "A" IN SLEEPING!?

SARCASM DOES NOT BECOME YOU, MA'AM!

YOU WERE RIGHT... I SPENT THE WHOLE AFTERNOON OUTSIDE, AND I HAD A GREAT TIME!

I WALKED ALL THE WAY DOWN TO WHERE THAT NEW APPLIANCE STORE IS

BEING OUTSIDE ALL AFTERNOON WASN'T AS BAD AS I THOUGHT IT WOULD BE

6-15

THE APPLIANCE STORE HAD A TV IN THE WINDOW!

© 1983 United Feature Syndicate, Inc.

I HAVE BEAUTIFUL MEMORIES OF OTHER SUMMER NIGHTS JUST LIKE THIS...

MY SWEET BABBOO AND I USED TO SIT OUT HERE ON THIS PORCH SWING HOLDING HANDS AND LISTENING TO THE MUSIC..

6-16

NO, WE DIDN'T!

WELL, WE SHOULD HAVE!!

© 1983 United Feature Syndicate, Inc.

OKAY, DOES EACH OF YOU HAVE A CAMERA?

GOOD! WE ARE NOW GOING ON WHAT IS CALLED A PHOTO HIKE

© 1983 United Feature Syndicate, Inc.

THE IDEA, OF COURSE, IS TO GIVE YOU THE CHANCE TO TAKE SOME BEAUTIFUL AND MAYBE UNUSUAL PICTURES...

6-20

NOT NECESSARILY OF YOURSELVES!

I JUST SAW YOUR STUPID DOG GO BY... WHERE'S HE GOING?

© 1983 United Feature Syndicate, Inc.

HE'S TAKING HIS FRIENDS TO "POINT LOBOS" ON A PHOTO HIKE...

6-21

"POINT LOBOS"?! DOESN'T HE KNOW HOW FAR THAT IS? HOW'S HE EVER GOING TO FIND IT?

IF IT'S THERE WHEN WE GET THERE, WE'LL KNOW WE'RE THERE

THE PLACE WE'RE GOING TO ON OUR PHOTO HIKE IS CALLED "POINT LOBOS"

THAT MEANS, "POINT OF THE SEA WOLVES"

6-22

© 1983 United Feature Syndicate, Inc.

WELL, THERE ISN'T ANY "POINT BUNNIES"!

THERE IT IS, GANG..THE PACIFIC OCEAN!

NOW, I WANT TO SEE YOU TAKE A LOT OF PICTURES..THAT'S WHAT WE'RE HERE FOR...

6-23

WHAT ARE YOU TAKING A PICTURE OF, OLIVIER... THE OCEAN? GOOD!

!?

NO, I CAN'T ASK IT TO SMILE

© 1983 United Feature Syndicate, Inc.

BEAUTIFUL, ISN'T IT?

MAYBE, WHEN WE GET BACK, YOU CAN SELL SOME OF YOUR PHOTOGRAPHS TO A WILDLIFE MAGAZINE...

© 1983 United Feature Syndicate. Inc.   6-27

WHAT'S WILDLIFE? YOU'RE WILDLIFE

I'M WHAT YOU CALL SEMI-WILDLIFE

WOW! LOOK AT THAT!

YOU SHOULD GET A SHOT OF THAT TREE, OLIVIER...TRY f/8 AT 1/125.....OKAY?

YOU MIGHT ALSO WANT TO USE A TRIPOD...

ME AND MY SUGGESTIONS..

6-28

© 1983 United Feature Syndicate, Inc.

SCHULZ

BILL AND HARRIET GOT MARRIED

7-1 © 1983 United Feature Syndicate, Inc.

WE CAME ALL THE WAY TO "POINT LOBOS" TO PHOTOGRAPH THE TREES, THE ROCKS, THE OCEAN...

AND WHAT DO WE GET?

WEDDING PICTURES!

CLICK SNAP SNAP CLICK! CLICK!

I TAKE MY TROOPS TO "POINT LOBOS" FOR A PHOTO HIKE, AND WHAT HAPPENS?

BILL AND HARRIET GET MARRIED, AND DECIDE TO STAY...

7-2

ANYWAY, IT WAS A BEAUTIFUL WEDDING... IT HAD TO BE...

I WAS "BEST BEAGLE"!

© 1983 United Feature Syndicate, Inc.